# MATH
## ON THE
# OUTSIDE

## Rob Vingerhoets

# THANKS TO:

- Mick Ymer for his hints and advice on bean-bag golf.
- Tim Field, whom I first saw take children for the game of bean-bag golf many, many moons ago.
- My wife and part-time personal editor, Marg, for her help, advice, and much appreciated encouragement.
- George Murdoch, my principal, for his substantial support, helpful ideas, and "public relations" work.
- Fiona Thorpe, for all her invaluable assistance and advice with the computer.
- My gorgeous baby daughter, Maddie, who at every opportunity single-handedly did her best to distract me from writing this book.

Published with the permission of Dellasta Pty. Ltd.
© revised 1993 Learning Resources, Inc., Lincolnshire, Illinois 60069.
First published 1991 by Dellasta Pty. Ltd., Mount Waverley, Victoria, Australia.

ISBN 156911-005-0 (previously ISBN 0 947 138 75 7)

Printed in the United States of America.

**LEARNING RESOURCES**

# OVERHEAD & MATH MANIPULATIVES

Enrich the activities in this book with the following manipulatives! See your local school supply dealer for more information on the complete line of Learning Resources' overhead and math products. For a dealer near you, call (800) 222-3909.

**LER 340**    **Trundle Wheel:** Use to measure long distances. Wheel is graduated in 5-cm intervals and has a nonslip rubber edge.

**LER 365**    **Wind-Up Tape:** Fiberglass tape is marked in cm and mm with in. on the reverse. Rolls into sturdy case.

**LER 303**    **Tape Measures:** Divided into decimeter segments, this 150-cm tape is a valuable tool. Its backside is calibrated in cm and mm (set of 10).

**LER 310**    **Centimeter Grids:** You can measure the area of objects or construct charts or maps with transparent flexible grids for the overhead projector.

**LER 640**    **Overhead Pattern Blocks:** This set of richly-colored transparent pieces is perfect for classroom problem solving.

**LER 1277**    **Attribute Block Desk Set:** 60-piece geometry set includes plastic storage box with compartments. Its lid doubles as a shape sorter.

**LER 336**    **Patternables:** 64-page fun-filled activity book provides plans for building pictures of animals and objects with pattern blocks.

**LER 952**    **MathLink™ Cubes:** High-quality plastic 2-cm cubes fit together easily on all sides. Great for lacing, patterning, basic operations, measuring, and problem solving.

**LER 54**    **Basic Student Calc-U-Vue:** Solar-powered calculator features 4 basic functions; 3-key memory; +/−, percent, and square root keys; floating decimal; constant functions; and 8-digit LCD display.

# Contents

# Introduction

Lately, much is written about real-life, active math and this booklet is all about that and getting some fresh air as well. It is also about math that is child generated, that involves group work and problem solving, and that is essentially *enjoyable.*

The math trails and bean-bag golf course described in these pages have been developed by the Grade 5/6 children in my room and myself over the past 2 years.

## *Math trails*

Math trails can be a great way of showing your children that math is all around them and that they really do know math — it's just that they haven't recognized it before or realized its connection with the work they do in the classroom.

Trails can be a very effective way of making children aware that math is *not* confined to the classroom. By becoming aware of math in their own environment and surroundings, children can learn to put math into a context, and through seeing a purpose and relevance to math, a more positive attitude towards it can be fostered.

Presented here are two examples of math trails and some additional ideas for school and home. The examples include pre-trail planning and activities, organizational hints, some "on the trail" mathematical possibilities, ideas on utilizing the trail effectively, and how best to evaluate the impact of the math trail.

## The *Bean-bag Golf* Course

The stimulus for my bean-bag golf course had its origins in a word game I play with the children. Through the playing of this game I was able to introduce the children to the fundamentals of the game of golf and to some of the basic terminology associated with golf. This is very important, with many of the children having heard of golf, but only a few of them having any knowledge of how to play the game.

The word golf game, described later, is a very stimulating introduction to real golf and to the bean-bag golf course — a course that children can design and build themselves.

# The community math trail

Depending on your location, setting up a math trail that takes the children not only out of the classroom but out of the immediate school grounds as well can be very worthwhile.

Most current math trails are teacher designed, established, and monitored, so why not try something different and allow the kids to set up their own math trail, with you, the teacher, acting as a consultant.

Developing their own trail involves the children in far more math, problem solving, and creativity than completing a trail already established. Furthermore, the trail they develop will not only be theirs but can readily be used by other grades in the school.

This involves a degree of risk taking on your part, but don't underestimate your students' ability to cope with the task. With you as a guide, they are very adept at identifying the math around them and planning a trail accordingly.

## Planning the trail

1 *Introduce the term math trail* Explain to the children what a math trail is all about. For example, you could say: "On a math trail you might be asked to look around you and find the answers to such questions as:
- For how many hours a day are you allowed to parallel park on __ __ __ Street?
- If the house next to the school is number 167, what will be the number on the fifth house from the school?
- What shape is the traffic sign at the end of __ __ __ Avenue?"

3

**2 *Put the idea to the children*** "What if you made a math trail for the other children in the school to follow?"

**3 *Describe a possible route*** "The trail could start at the front gate of the school, then go up __ __ __ Road to the crossing, then come back the other side to __ __ __ Avenue, then go along that to __ __ __ Street, then finish at the back gate of the school." Discuss the route.

**4 *Consider the possibilities*** Point out, or better still, have the troops point out what sort of things they could look out for along the way that have anything to do with math. (It may be necessary to discuss with the children that this doesn't just mean things to do with numbers but can be shapes, times, estimations of distances, and other measurement areas.) Don't be disappointed if the children come up with limited suggestions. While they are walking the prospective trail, they will see the many mathematical possibilities.

**5 *A mini-trail*** To give the children an illustration and a feel for what the trail is about, make up a sample trail in your own room. Draw up a sheet for a small group of children and have them do the trail.

For example, "Start at the door. How tall do you think it is? (_____) Follow the right-hand wall. How many windows along this wall? (_____) Go to the front of the room. What shape is the blackboard? (_____) How long do you think it is? (_____) How many books are there in the top row of the bookshelf? (_____) Go to the back of the room and estimate the perimeter of Mr. V's desk. (_____)," etc.

Include about ten tasks on this mini-trail and have the answers ready to give to the children once they have all finished the trail. Ask the children to look around for other ideas and questions that could have been included on this room mini-trail.

**6 *Map the trail*** Before taking the troops along the community trail (if you and the children have already agreed on a certain route), get them to make a map of the designated trail or have them make up maps for the trails they have designed themselves. Do this in pairs or small groups.

While it is up to you how detailed you wish these maps to be, they should be drawn to scale reasonably accurately and should include any major features and street names, and proportional representations of the lengths of streets and sizes of houses and parks and so on, compared with the size of the school.

Having the children map the trail, either the one chosen by the whole grade or their own ideas of where the trail could go, involves them from

4

the outset in some basic math work (scale, measuring, planning, visual representation) on an undertaking that is going to be initiated by them and is of direct interest to them. It also starts the children thinking about those buildings, shops, bridges, parks, or other features on the route that could be part of the math trail. (You may find a local street directory comes in handy.)

Display and discuss the resultant maps.

If a particular route has not previously been decided upon, use the children's maps as a basis to design one.

## Some pre-trail organization

With the concept of a math trail now explained and exemplified, and having established the final route of the trail and run through some possible things to look for while on it, the obvious next step is to hit the trail. Whoa! Hang on a minute; a few considerations may be well worthwhile:

1   What about telling the principal about the idea and getting his or her support? While you're at it, check that you have permission to take the children outside the school grounds. Many schools have a local excursion notice that covers the children for small trips and excursions (such as sports visits, walks to the supermarket, etc.), and this should also cover the children while on the trail. If this is not available, you may need to draw up a permission notice for parents to sign.

2   Consider asking/begging the vice principal, the teacher next door, or anybody else who owes you a favor to watch at least half your grade (two-thirds would be better, but don't push your luck!) while you take the remainder on the trail. It is quite feasible to take the whole grade, but you will find it more beneficial to take groups of eight to thirteen children so you can provide more help and advice and more effectively supervise them.

3   Have you anticipated the time you will need to take the children on the trail? This is especially important if you have managed to convince, connive, or cajole someone into looking after part of your grade. Depending on the length of the trail, 1 hour will usually be quite sufficient.

4   Have you considered the safety aspects? Are all roads you may need to cross comparatively safe? Can you make use of any pedestrian crossings or traffic lights? Will you be able to view the children at all times? Do you pass by a house containing a dog that is threatening?

## Preparation

Ensure that the children are physically prepared before going on the trail. They will need a pen, a back-up pen, paper, and something solid to lean the paper on. I found notepads worked quite well, or providing the children with clips will prevent valuable work from blowing off into the stratosphere.

Take along a couple of meter rulers and trundle wheels as you will find that the children will want to use them.

Be wary of the weather and have the kids dress appropriately.

## Recording observations

Since their mission, should they choose to accept it, is to observe and note things mathematical so that these may form part of their math trail, it would be well worthwhile to explain to the children some effective ways of recording their observations:

- They could write down their observations in the form of questions — ultimately this is the form they will be in anyway, so why not do it from the beginning? Children should ensure that they write down the answer, if known, as well as the question, or make note of the fact that they need to find the answer by asking their friends or the teacher during or after the trail.
  *Example:* One girl is walking past a dentist's office and spots something she thinks could be part of the trail —

  "What is the largest number you can make out of the dentist's phone number?"

  The child should then either write down the answer or make note of the phone number and work out the answer later on.
- Simply observing and noting things without the onus and pressure of turning them into questions may prove the more successful method for some children. In their case it is far better to be keenly looking for the math about them and noting it. Back in the classroom these written observations can readily be turned into questions.
  *Example:* One child spots the telephone number of the dentist's office — 583-8207 — and notes it. He thinks that he might be able to turn that into a question at a later stage. Back in the room, and with help and advice if needed, the question can be formulated:

  "What is the largest number you can make from the dentist's phone number?"

On the point of writing questions/observations, emphasize to the children the need to place the questions/observations in a clear sequence and

6

to provide location clues at all times. Nobody should have to go backwards when doing a trail and nobody should have to try to answer a question such as: "How long is the fence?"

"Estimate the length of the brick fence at 62 Frank St." is a far more appropriate question/task.

## Math on the trail

### Ready to go? — A summary

Hitting the trail and spotting the math are what the troops will be very keen to do, and if you have the necessary organizational aspects covered, there's basically nothing stopping you.

Rally the children at a specified place, for example, in front of the office or near the parking lot. They will possibly be a little excited at the prospect of a romp around the neighborhood, so it may be a good idea to tell them again that their job is to look for anything to do with math that they think could be part of a math trail and to write their observations down either as questions (making sure the answers are included if they can) or simply to write down the mathematical things they see and turn them into questions later.

Also remind the troops that not only the Grade 5 and 6 students, but the Grade 3 or 1 students, could go on the trail if they are informed and invited. So tell them not to worry about writing down anything they think is too easy as the questions might suit the children from another grade.

## Your role as their teacher/consultant

- Tell the children not to wander too far ahead or linger too far behind.
- Act as a timekeeper and keep the troops moving, without preventing them from noticing the math around them.
- Be available to answer their questions and reinforce and encourage their observations, since they are generally a little unsure of themselves on this initial expedition.
- Encourage the children to look at more than the footpath or the road and to really open their eyes and have a good look around.
- Observe the children. Note whether they are working together, how much they are enjoying the activity, and how well they are identifying the math around them.
- *Be patient and be quiet!* There will be things the children walk straight past that you know would be great on the trail. It will be very difficult to stop yourself from pointing these out to one of the troops, *but* it is *their* trail and the math and subsequent questions for the trail should come from them.

    Take into account that the next group from your room may spot what this group has missed.

    You can bet on the fact that while the children will miss things you can see, they will also come up with things that hadn't even occurred to you.

Consider also that it is very advisable to take the children on the trail to gather questions at least twice. On the second trip the children are more adept at searching for and finding questions (which may have been missed on the first occasion) and they invariably add many questions to their original lists. It also gives them an additional opportunity to check up on answers they may not have gained initially and to ensure they have given accurate location directions.

## Sample questions

Of course, questions will vary from school location to school location, but the following is a small sample of the questions the children in my grade wrote when preparing our community math trail (they are not in any sequence). They achieved these questions on two journeys of the trail in small groups, and one revisional trip as a whole grade during which we "fine tuned" the questions and answers.

- How long are each of the parking spaces in front of the stores?
- What shape is the stop sign on Summer St.?
- How many hours in a week is the grocery store open?

- How tall is the yield sign at the end of Burnside St.?
- What shape is it?
- Which car license plate has the largest number out of all the cars in the parking lot?
- When you pass the telephone booth in front of the drugstore, find out what it costs to make a local call.
- What is the sixth number of the phone number on the dumpster?
- How many mailboxes are there at the apartment building?
- The open lot on the corner of Summer St. is 146 meters long. How many houses do you think you could fit on it?
- What is the most expensive house for sale in the window of the real-estate agent?
- Count the cars in the parking lot. Not counting the spares, how many tires is that?
- How high is the fence at the front of the school?
- How tall are the bicycle rack signs in front of the shop?
- Look at the big green sign post in Ballarat Rd. How far is it to Melton? How far is it from Bacchus Marsh to Adelaide? How far is it from Melton to Ballarat?
- If you bought all the items advertised in the windows of Tucker Bag, how much would it cost you?
- Find the number of the Western Highway and then multiply it by 6.
- Find the number of the house next to the church and double it.
- Estimate how far it is between the two speed bumps in front of St. Peter Chanel school.
- Guess how tall the mailbox is at the house at 844 Ballarat Rd.
- Look at the gas station. How much is gas per gallon? What would 10 gallons cost?
- At the gas station, what is the difference in price for a gallon of super unleaded and a gallon of regular unleaded gas?

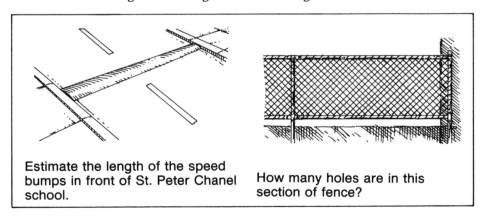

Estimate the length of the speed bumps in front of St. Peter Chanel school.

How many holes are in this section of fence?

- Estimate the perimeter of the vacant lot next to the school. Clue — the front of the lot is 42 meters.
- What time is the pizza shop open till on Sundays?
- Guess how long the green walk signal stays green at the St. Peter Chanel crossing.
- How many big square windows are there at the two-story house at 830 Ballarat Rd.?
- How long do you think the math trail was?

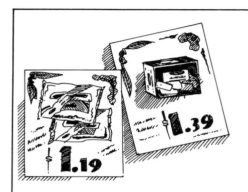

Add up the prices of the specials in the windows of Tucker Bag.

What is the cheapest house for sale in the window of the real-estate agent?

## Polishing the product

After each journey along the trail, I asked the children back in the classroom to go over their questions or observations. This gave them an opportunity to improve their questions and write them in a clear and well-presented way, something that is obviously difficult to do while on the trail. The children should ensure that all their questions make sense and have answers (except for any open-ended questions).

The chart *You've got it covered* illustrates how the questions developed by the children involve most of the prescribed areas of math.

10

# You've got it covered

The community math trail

## Counting

- Reading house and phone numbers, car license plates
- Writing down large numbers in words and numerals

## Operations/Computations

- Using estimation and mental computations in practical situations
- Using operations to calculate area/perimeter
- Using the calculator where appropriate

## Place value

- Making largest/smallest numbers from phone numbers
- Ordering car license plates
- Renaming numbers
- Converting money and length measurements

## Problem solving

- Planning the trail and designing the route
- Investigating and identifying the math
- Checking solutions
- Organizing themselves and others

## Spatial relations

- Recognizing shapes in architecture — roofs, fences, etc.
- Identifying the shapes of various traffic signs
- Planning/sketching a route for the trail

## Visual representation

- Reading/interpreting sign posts
- Designing a map of the proposed route for the trail
- Reading street directory and community information maps

## Pattern and order

- Recognizing odd/even patterns for house numbers and continuing these
- Ordering house and car license plate numbers
- Investigating geometric patterns and shapes in the architecture of buildings, fences, windows

## Measurement

- Estimating and measuring lengths of a number of objects
- Estimating perimeter and area of objects
- Time — interpreting parking signs, calculating times/distances from sign posts
- Money — totaling prices on store ads, ordering prices

Those items listed under each of the headings are by no means prescriptive, as there will no doubt be many other items that could be added to the lists. The examples merely exemplify the broad range of mathematical topics that are or can be incorporated into the math trail.

## Safety first

On a third trip, with the whole grade, I had the children from my grade consider the safety aspects of the trail. They were asked to note down any potential dangers they observed or recalled from the two previous trips.

This is particularly important if you intend to invite children in lower grades on the trail.

These are some of the safety hints the grade developed:

- Don't run.
- When you approach houses, always look to see whether there are cars coming out of the driveway.
- If the teachers are slow, wait for them to catch up; don't cross any roads without them.
- When looking for answers, stay on the footpath but not in the driveways.
- Where there is a pedestrian crossing make sure you use it, and when you use the crossing at St. Peter Chanel, split into two groups as you only have 8 seconds to get across.

# Making the math trail effective

## Sorting the questions

Now that you're armed with a large supply of questions and answers, the next move is to sort these questions into appropriate grade/year levels. Perhaps a committee of four to six children, with your assistance if needed, could have the task of sorting through the questions and classifying them into those questions suitable to Grades 5 and 6, those suitable to Grades 3 and 4, and those suitable to Grades K, 1, and 2.

While grouping the questions, the sorting committee should delete those questions that are poorly written or do not make sense. They should also alter, where necessary, those questions that may need a locational clue or may need to be slightly reworded.

## Come on — try the trail

After the questions have been sorted and checked and agreed to, those for each area could then be typed onto one or two sheets. A separate sheet for the corresponding answers to each area's questions should also be typed up. (Perhaps a teacher aide could do this typing or have the children themselves do it on a computer and print it out.) Finally, include with the question and answer sheets a page with the safety tips mentioned earlier.

Now that the completed math trail packages are ready to deliver, the remaining task involves promoting the math trail and encouraging other grades to try it. This becomes a matter of advertising the trail, which can readily be done with a series of visits to classrooms by a group of children prepared to describe the trail and the type of fun stuff you can do on it.

Particularly with Grades K, 1, and 2 and even Grades 3 and 4, I found it a very worthwhile idea to make the offer to teachers of having two or three children from my room go with their grades to act as helpers/guides.

This not only promoted responsibility in my troops but also significantly assisted the teachers and the children during the trail through helping with supervision and providing advice (only where necessary).

Furthermore, the guides were able to report back on how the grades they accompanied on the trail coped with the questions and how much or little the children enjoyed the trail. This occasionally resulted in alterations being made to various questions to make them more suitable.

## Spreading the word

To make a truly effective math trail, why stop at letting the other teachers and children in the school know about it? Tell the parents about the trail. Have a couple of children from your room write a paragraph or two to be placed in the weekly newsletter. A map could be included to make the parents more aware. During Education Week set up the trail and invite the parents to try it.

If you happen to have a nearby school that you have some sort of regular contact with, you may wish to invite the staff to send a grade to try out the trail. This not only is good PR but also may encourage that school to set up a trail of its own that you and your troops could eventually try out.

With some pictures and an accompanying story, the local newspapers are likely to be interested enough to publish an article on your math trail. This spreading of the word promotes an awareness of math as well as what is happening at your school, and it is through this increased awareness that the effectiveness of your trail is developed.

# Evaluating the math trail

## What to evaluate?

On a relatively major undertaking such as developing a math trail, there are several aspects to consider when trying to evaluate the trail. These may include the following:

**1** *Cooperation*　Group work is a major feature of the trail, with the children needing/wanting to discuss their questions and answers, with a group having the responsibility of classifying the questions into appropriate grade areas, and with children needing to work cooperatively with other children and teachers from various grades.

Observing the children in these cooperative situations can be very enlightening in terms of respect for each other's feelings and opinions, tolerance of differing opinions, valuing the opinions and ideas of others, and generally accepting their role in a team and being contributors to the team effort. (I found I learned a lot about the children in my room by observing and noting down their behavior in these cooperative situations.)

*I really liked taking the other grades around on the trail.*　Vicki

**2** *Responsibility*　By its nature, the development of the math trail entails the children working for a goal that is almost entirely dependent on their input. If they want to make up a trail, then they have to do the work, and given that it is an enjoyable experience walking around their community, and that there are numerous opportunities to be distracted from the task, it really requires an effort by the troops to make sure the job is done.

You will probably find with our children that they are aware of this responsibility and tend to keep each other on the job, as they realize that the success of the trail depends on them.

Writing items for the newsletter, promoting the trail in other grades, and acting as helpers/guides on the trail are all significant opportunities for children to display a sense of responsibility, and noting how the children concerned coped with these responsibilities can be quite worthwhile.

*It was great fun going around and looking for math around the streets.*　Sonia

**3 _Language_** From the many discussions that take place regarding the math that may exist on the trail, to the formulation of questions and answers, to the promoting of the trail in oral and written forms, to the communication with children from other grades, language skills are integral to the development of the trail. The degree of emphasis you place on the evaluation of these skills is a matter of choice, but it would be unwise not to recognize the strong links between math and language.

_We found lots of stuff on the walk that had something to do with math. – Kevin_

**4 _Problem solving_** Apart from the development of measurement, number, shape, and estimation skills, working on the math trail involves children in a great deal of problem solving. The skills associated with this problem solving included:

- _designing_ — maps of the trail, format for the questions and answers;
- _organizing and planning_ — what questions to choose for the grade levels, setting out the questions to include location clues and to be sequential, how to promote the trail, a roster for the guides for other grades;
- _anticipating_ — predicting possible safety problems on the trail and questions with which the children may require extra assistance;
- _applying strategies_ — discussing, applying, and evaluating ways to organize the trail and then applying again the most practical and efficient ones; this includes the children learning from mistakes made initially.

_It was fun doing math out of the room._
_Con_

_Making a math trail was great._
_Brendan_

**5 _Awareness and attitude_** One of the most beneficial attributes of the development of a community math trail should be an increased awareness in the children, particularly those who established the trail, of the math around them. In turn, the children coming to appreciate that math is related to the real world and is not necessarily only something associated with a check or X on a test is the ultimate aspect of the math trail to evaluate. Therefore, observing the children enjoying and being positive about math while applying essential mathematical skills such as estimating, calculating, measuring, recording their work, and problem solving will be your own personal and most significant evaluation.

# A school math trail

If your local community does not lend itself to a math trail (your school may be in an isolated area with very little surrounding it or next to a dump or a swamp or something), then setting up a math trail within the school grounds may be a possibility.

A school math trail can be a lot of fun without being as detailed as the community version. It may not incorporate as many areas of or as much math, but it still allows the children to discover that math is alive and well in their own environment.

As with the community trail, allow the children to discover the math while you act as their guide and consultant. This ownership of the finished product has many inherent attributes, not the least of which is an increased motivation to do the job well.

There may appear to be less potential for math on the school grounds as compared with the community trail, but be wary of underestimating the imagination and observation skills of the children in your class.

While there is nothing to prevent you from developing trails both outside and inside the school grounds – they both can be done in the same year or in alternate years as I had the children in my room do – establishing a math trail within the school has the following advantages:

- There is no need to address all the organizational aspects of taking the children beyond the school grounds. This in turn allows you more freedom to take the children outside at any time of your choice and to spend more time outside if required.
- There are fewer safety problems encountered taking the whole grade out into the school grounds — no roads to cross, no supervising the troops while they are spread out along a sidewalk.

17

- Where it was advisable, if not essential, to take the children in smaller groups on the community trail, it is quite feasible to take the whole grade into the school yard where they may then be broken up into three or four smaller groups.
- A school math trail, not being as long in distance or as involved as the community version, allows you and the children the opportunity to utilize more equipment and thoroughly search for the math that is concentrated in a smaller area.

The major disadvantage is that there are generally fewer and less varied mathematical opportunities within the school yard.

# Planning the trail

## Introduce the term

If the school math trail is not the children's first trail, this will not be necessary; otherwise refer to the *Planning the trail section* of "The community *math trail*."

## Put the idea to the children

Even if the children have already developed a community trail, present them with the idea of setting one up within the school. Tell the children that they are going to find as many things as possible to do with math around the school. They could make these things part of a trail that children in other grades could go on.

## Consider the possibilities

Ask the children to try to think of anything around the school that may have anything to do with math. Don't be disappointed if they come up with only a small number of possibilities, particularly if this is their initial math trail and they haven't the experience gained from developing a community trail.

Things that are mathematically orientated around the school will not spring readily to mind. The children may put forward ideas such as counting the number of windows in the school, guessing how tall the flag pole is, or how long a wall is or other objects to do with length. Accept any ideas and provide plenty of encouragement.

## Check out the territory

Take the troops outside for a stroll around the school. Precede the stroll by asking them to have a good look around them, even though they have no doubt seen everything a thousand times before, and to take mental notes of anything that they consider could have anything to do with math. Walk them around all areas of the school: near the buildings, along the fences, on the grounds, by the playground equipment, and to any other areas of potential interest.

If you find the children are having difficulty identifying objects with mathematical possibilities, despite being encouraged to look closely at all things around them, it may be worthwhile to ask appropriately leading questions to get them looking and thinking more.
For example:
"What shape is the basketball court?"
"How many bricks are in that wall and how can I work it out without counting every single brick?"
"Estimate the perimeter of the sand pit."

Asking these types of questions gives the children examples of the type of math they could be looking for and often results in their needing very little subsequent prompting.

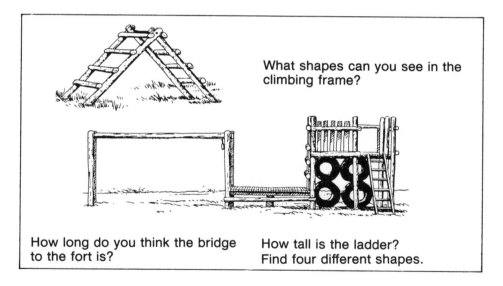

What shapes can you see in the climbing frame?

How long do you think the bridge to the fort is?

How tall is the ladder?
Find four different shapes.

# Math on the trail

## Some small-group discovery

After you and the troops have returned from the stroll outside, have them give you some examples of the type of questions or math they thought of.

Record some of these on the board and discuss them with the children. Now that they have a clear idea of what is required, have them form groups of three or four. Inform the groups that their mission is to go out of the room and explore the school grounds and find as many things as they can that have anything to do with math, record these, and then turn them into questions.

To help to ensure that my children knew what I was talking about and to facilitate a common approach to the collection and recording of the questions, I issued them a question sheet, part of which is shown in Figure 1. (A full-page example is included as Appendix 3.)

| Object or place | Location | Question | Answer |
|---|---|---|---|
|  |  |  |  |

**Figure 1**   Part of the question sheet issued to the children planning the trail

I then allocated the groups an hour and a half, during which time they were to find as much math as possible, record the location of the math they found, turn the math into questions, and ensure that each of those questions had an answer.

The children were asked to consider what equipment they might need before setting off, and subsequently they requested trundle wheels, rulers, measuring tapes (large and small), calculators, and other assorted items. (As it turned out, some of the groups asked if they could borrow things such as the bow calipers for measuring diameter, the scales and weights, and the measuring jugs.)

With their sheets, necessary equipment, and a good idea of what was expected and what to look for, from their initial whole-grade stroll and follow-up discussions, the groups of intrepid math explorers then set off into the wilds of the school yard.

The teacher's role during this time should be one of wandering among the groups, generally supervising and giving help and advice – *when asked!*

Following are some examples of the sort of things my troops came up with on this initial tour in their small groups:

Some of the questions have been modified slightly to accommodate the format, but basically they exemplify the types of questions the groups came up with.

20

| Object or place | Location | Question | Answer |
|---|---|---|---|
| 1 Soccer field | On the field | What's the name of the shape in front of the goal? | A rectangle |
| 2 Front of the kinder-garten | At the kinder-garten | How many windows are there altogether at the front of the building? | 2 rows of 6 × 4 rooms = 48 |
| 3 The fort | Near the new equipment | How high is it from the ground to the top? | 2 m 15 cm |
| 4 The back fence | Back of the school | How many holes are in the section of fence behind the goals? | 186 × 48 = 8928 (calculator) |
| 5 Long jump pit | On the school track | Estimate the perimeter of the long jump pit. | 47 m |
| 6 The tennis court | On the court area | Count how many rectangles there are on a tennis court. | 16 *Hint:* (Squares are rectangles) |
| 7 The tree in front of the boys' bath-room | Near the boys' bathroom, in front of the water fountain | What is the circumference of the tree in front of the boys' bathroom? | 2 m 77 cm |
| 8 The dump-ster | At the side of the school | Find the phone number on the dumpster and make the largest number you can. | 9 754 431 |
| 9 The sand pit | In front of room 3 | Estimate the area of the sand pit. | 21 sq m |
| 10 The basket-ball court | On the court area | How far is it from anywhere on the 3 point to a spot directly underneath the basket? | 6.25 m |

The range of questions the children develop will be determined to a large extent by work done previously in the classroom. The children in my room had experience with diameter, circumference, and other measurement areas such as mass, length, and capacity, and knowledge of this prior work was evident in their questions.

Depending on the quality and quantity of questions developed by the troops on this initial journey, it may not be necessary to have them go outside again, although some groups may wish to check answers or re-state location directions.

## Sorting the questions

Provide the groups with the opportunity to review the wording of their questions, check that they have answers to all the questions, and that all the answers are checked.

Next organize the children so they are working with another group. Each pair of groups should be asked to do the following:

1 To compare questions to make sure that both groups did not have the same questions.

2 To check that their answers were the same, if they did have the same question.

3 To check to see whether either group had different questions about the same object or place, for example, estimate the length of the basketball court and what is the area of one of the backboards on the basketball court.

4 To exchange question sheets and discuss each other's questions. Other groups may spot previously missed errors or suggest worthwhile ways to improve some questions.

Then provide each pair of groups with two or three blank question sheets and have each group choose one person to act as a recorder. The task of the two recorders, with the assistance of the others, is to write out all the questions gathered by the two groups:

• leaving out repeated questions;
• grouping together questions based on the same object or place;
• taking into account any alterations made to improve the questions.

## A question committee

Once the question sheets from each pair of groups have been collected (there may be three to six sets of sheets to collect depending on the size of your grade or the size of the groups), it can now be the job of a group of children — three is a good number — to go through all the corrected questions. As with the previous review of the questions, they will need to:

1 check for and leave out any repeated questions;

22

2 group together any questions based on the same object or place;

3 reword or have the original writers rewrite any questions that are hard to follow;

4 make any alterations necessary to improve any of the questions;

5 check for any answers that don't appear to make sense and test them if necessary;

6 present the final list of questions in an organized and easy-to-read format.

## Which way do we go?

Now that there is a final list of questions, the next step is to place these in a designated order. By deciding on a definite route or pathway around the school, the questions then can be organized to match the places and objects encountered along the route. Present a possible route to be considered. The route may be proposed by the whole grade, by yourself, or even as recommended by a small committee.

The following example is part of the route the troops decided on when developing a trail for our school:

Starting at the front office, walk past the mural along the path between the parking lot and the lunchroom. Go past the multi-purpose room and turn left toward the kindergarten. Turn right and go down the steps in front of the kindergarten and follow the path past the sandpit and go onto the basketball court, etc., etc.

Discuss the route in detail, and when a consensus (or close enough to a consensus!) has been reached, either have another small committee of three or four or the whole grade order the questions as the occur along the route. It may develop along lines similar to this (using the above example).

| *Route* | *Questions* |
|---|---|
| "We're starting at the office area at the front of the school." | 1 Add up the numbers in our school number; is the answer odd or even? |
| "We go past the mural." | No questions |
| "Walk along the path between the parking lot and the lunchroom." | 2 Which car has the highest license number in the parking lot? |
| | 3 Not counting spares, how many tires are in this parking lot? |
| "Go past the multi-purpose room." | 4 What shape is the top window at the front of the multi-purpose room? |

Continue this process until all or most of the questions are matched to places or objects along the agreed route.

You and the children may find that:

- the proposed route cannot cater to every question, and it may be necessary to delete some questions, as they concern objects that would involve a major deviation from the trail;
- there may be a section of the proposed route along which there are few, if any, questions — this may require the children to develop some additional questions for this area or change the route of the trail.

## Making the trail effective

### What have we got?

At this stage we should have:

- a set of clearly written and checked-out questions covering places and objects from all around the school;
- an agreed-on route for around the school;
- a matching of questions to the places and objects encompassed on the route;
- a worthwhile appreciation of just how much math is all around us and an increasing awareness that math can be relevant and enjoyable too.

### What do we still need?

One very useful item that should now be produced is a reasonably accurate map of the school. This map could show clearly the proposed route of the math trail and the direction any participants in the trail should take.

Rather than reinvent the wheel, check and see whether the office has a copy of a layout of the school buildings. (Emergency plans often include a layout of the school buildings and grounds.)

Using the layout as a base, draw or mark in additional required features (e.g., the tree in front of the boys' bathroom or the dumpster or the fort and the playground equipment), and using arrows or marked lines, draw in the route and direction of the trail.

If no map is available to use as a basis, it can be a most challenging and worthwhile activity to have the children work in small groups to construct a map of the school. (Appendix 4 shows the school layout for my particular school. The children used the layout as a basis for a map including all places and objects found on their trail.)

## Try the trail

Now that we have a set of questions and a map of the school, the obvious thing to do is to see how well they correspond. This is essential as you will eventually be issuing copies of the map and questions to prospective users of the school math trail.

There is probably no better way to find any faults or vagaries of the math trail than to physically try it. Take the children outside, together with a map of the school and a list of the questions, and organize them into their original small groups. It is then a matter of each of the groups following the map while using the questions as a guide to what exactly they should be looking for, for example:

**Dave**  The map says we should be walking along the path that goes in front of the new play equipment and stop there.

**Dave**  OK, now we have to go over to the long jump pit on the school track.

**Jane**  There are some questions for the play equipment:
1  What shape is the climbing frame?
2  How long do you think the bridge that joins the two forts is?

**Jane**  That's right. The next thing it says to do is:
3  Estimate the perimeter of the long jump pit.

*Note:* Encourage the groups to look carefully for any faults and make note of these so they can be corrected before other grades are invited to go on the math trail.

## Reading the map

On the map my troops prepared, where they wanted or anticipated the participating trailers to stop and answer the questions, the word STOP was simply and appropriately written on the map.

Another possible method of ensuring that the questions correspond accurately to places and objects on the map and that the people doing the trail actually stop and answer the assigned questions for that spot is to code the map; an example is given in Figure 2.

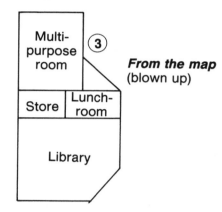

**From the question sheet**

**(3)  The Multi-purpose room**

Question 4. What is the shape of the top window at the front of the multi-purpose room?

**From the map**
(blown up)

**Figure 2**  Coding used to indicate the site of a question

This way, the people on the trail realize that when they reach the point marked (3), they need to stop and look up the question/s marked (3) and try to answer them. Similarly, when they reach the point on the map marked (4), they will need to stop and find the question/s marked (4) on their question sheet, etc.

One of my children had suggested placing the questions on the same sheet as the map, but we soon found there were too many questions to fit and also there would not have been any space to write in answers or estimates.

Part of the question and answer sheet that accompanied the map is shown in Figure 3. (A blank question and answer sheet is given in Appendix 5.)

| Question | Working-out space | Answer |
|---|---|---|
| Question 12. How many bricks are there in the section of paving in front of the Art Room? | | |

**Figure 3**  Part of the question sheet that goes with the map

## Well, how did it go?

Ascertaining whether there were any significant faults that can be rectified or any minor errors that require some adjustment was the next task. We did this as a whole grade after first discussing, at length, how the trail generally worked. Overall the children were very happy and quite proud at the way the trail seemed to work so effectively. Then, again, they knew what to look for and what to expect but how would people new to the trail cope? There seemed only one way to find out.

## Testing the trail

It was decided that we should invite a group of six Grade 5/6 children from a neighboring room to test out the trail. As the children had decided it was best to work with a partner when doing the trail, we had the six volunteers work in pairs. Three of the children from my room accompanied the six, one for each pair, to observe and note down any difficulties encountered by the pair testing the trail.

The three observers reported back to the grade, and on the basis of this report, some more final adjustments and alterations were made to the trail, such as:

- changing the wording of some of the questions to make them easier to understand;
- clearly marking on the maps in what direction to start walking at the beginning of the trail;
- better drawing of some of the objects on the map (e.g., the fort) as children couldn't identify them, even though the questions were usually able to clear up any confusions.

The observers also recommended that at least one of them should accompany any future new trailers, based on the fact that they were able to clear up any problems because they were out there with the children doing the trail. If they were to act as guides — as for the community math trail — they could deal with any problems on the spot. Hard to argue with logic like that, so it was decided to adopt that recommendation.

## Promoting the trail

There seemed little left to do except get others involved in the school math trail. The children had worked hard and well at developing the trail and it would now be their task to advertise the trail within the school. You can refer to the *Come on – try the trail* and *Spreading the Word* sections of "The community *math trail*" chapter for details of this.

## Evaluation

The same areas that apply to evaluating the children when doing the community trail apply to the school trail, namely:

Cooperation
Responsibility
Language
Problem solving
Awareness and attitude.

The *Evaluating the math trail* section of "The community *math trail*" chapter details the above areas.

# Other trails

## Teacher generated

### A local park

Visit a local park and make up a trail for the children to do. Since this trail is designed by the teacher, it can directly reflect work that is or has taken place in the room. If you and the children have been working on diameter and circumference, for instance, you can readily structure questions on the park trail to reinforce those areas. For example: "Go to the tree next to the bench and estimate its circumference; how can you measure it?" Or "Use the bow caliper to find the diameter of the log near the barbecue."

Volume, capacity, area, and shape problems, as well as the more common length problems, may all be incorporated into a math trail at a local park.

It requires a fair amount of work on your part to survey the sight, design the questions, and organize the visit for your children, but the effort is generally well worth it.

### Camps or excursions

If you know you are going to a particular place, such as a campsite, it may be possible either to visit it beforehand and plan out a math trail or have some idea of what questions you could employ on the trail, and complete the trail upon arrival at the camp.

A math trail at a camp can be a lot of fun as well as increase the childrens awareness of math around them. Since it is teacher generated, a math trail can also revise or give the children the opportunity to practice their number and measurement skills.

# Established trails

Depending on where you live, there may be already established math trails that you could take your children to participate in. The zoo or city mall may well be places where a math trail has been established for use by schoolchildren and the general public.

# Around the home

Houses are interesting places normally full of math. From the shape of the TV to the capacity of the kitchen sink, to finding the bag or jar with the greatest mass in the pantry, to the area of your bed, to estimating the height of the house, to finding the container with the smallest capacity in the fridge, there are numerous mathematical opportunities. So encourage the children to work with their parents to make up a math trail around the home for other members of the family or neighbors (if they're welcome!) to try out.

# The *bean-bag golf* course

### The *word golf* game

The inspiration for my bean-bag golf course arose from the game of word golf, which my children find stimulating and enjoyable.

To indicate how the word game inspired the golf course, and as an added bonus at no extra cost to you, the reader, an explanation of the word golf game follows here:

**1** Open any book and randomly select the first two letters from nine words, for example, *sp*ort , *ov*erlap, *pr*epared, *sc*ope, *or*ganize, *in*dividual, *di*fferent, *th*inking, *fl*exible.

**2** Write these nine word beginnings vertically down the board:

> *sp*
> *ov*
> *pr*
> *sc*
> *or*
> *in*
> *di*
> *th*
> *fl*

**3** Now tell the troops that the object of the game is to try to make words using each of the two-letter beginnings *but* using as *few* letters as possible when completing the word.

Draw comparisons with the game of golf, in which the object is to get the ball into the hole in as few shots as possible and the lowest, not highest, score wins.

30

**4** Do a couple of examples with the children: "Here are the first two letters, *sp* — now try to make a word, using these two letters at the start, and using as few letters as you can."

One child may volunteer the word *space*. "O.K., that means you added on three letters — a,c,e — so your score for that hole is 3. Can anybody make a word using fewer than three letters?"

Another child may suggest the word *spot*. "Well done, your score would be 2 because you took two letters to finish the word. It is possible to complete this word in one letter, a hole in one. Can anyone do it?"

By this time the children usually get the idea of what's required and someone will put forward the word *spy*. "Great stuff! That's a hole in one. You added on only one letter, y, so your score for that hole would be 1."

Do another one or two examples with the children to ensure that they all understand how to play.

**5** *Par for the course* At this stage, I introduced the word par to the children. This was done by telling them that they should have completed the beginning *sp* with no more than two letters. Words like *spot, spit, spin* could all have been used to finish the word in two. On a real golf course all the holes have a par and that tells the golfer how many shots it *should* take to complete the hole.

A golfer may be playing a par 4 hole and that means he or she should get the ball in the hole in no more than four strokes. With one of the beginnings on the board, I may decide that you should finish it in no more than four letters, so the par for that beginning would be 4.

**6** *Birdies and bogeys* I told the children that for the beginning *sp*, I thought they should have finished it in no more than two letters, so that meant it was a *par* 2 beginning. Nicole suggested the word *spot* so she scored 2 and that was a par. Heath, who suggested the sword *space*, took three letters when he should have done it in two. That means he was one over a par, and another name for that is a *bogey*.

Brendan came up with the word *spy*, which was a score of 1. That means he completed the beginning in only one letter when I thought it would probably take two letters, so he's done really well and scored a 1 under the par, and that's known in golf as a *birdie*.

You will no doubt find that the children thoroughly enjoy these terms and think they're "weird." Allow them to discuss the scores and the terminology and ask any questions.

**7** **_Back to the Game_** Refer children to the original nine word beginnings on the board, and tell them that next to each beginning you are going to write the par for that "hole" or beginning:

| | |
|---|---|
| *sp* | (par 2) |
| *ov* | (par 2) |
| *pr* | (par 3) |
| *sc* | (par 3) |
| *or* | (par 3) |
| *in* | (par 2) |
| *di* | (par 1) |
| *th* | (par 3) |
| *fl* | (par 1) |

Try to give the troops the chance to score birdies with beginnings that are challenging without being too difficult; for example, *sc* may readily be completed with _ _ rap, _ _ ope, _ _ ale, _ _ arf, _ _ out, etc., for a par score, while a little thinking and adding _ _ ar or _ _ an can get you a birdie.

With the *di* beginning, I have made it a par 1 because if the children are thinking, they should readily get this in one by adding *e, g, p, m, d,* etc.

Add up all the pars for the nine holes or beginnings and inform the children that the par for this nine-hole golf course is 20 so that's how many letters they *should* use altogether to complete the beginnings. If they can do it in less than twenty letters, they beat the course, but anything over twenty means the course has beaten them.

**8** **_The board_** The chalkboard or whatever board you are using should now look like this at the start of play:

| | | |
|---|---|---|
| Hole 1 | *sp* | (par 2) |
| Hole 2 | *ov* | (par 2) |
| Hole 3 | *pr* | (par 3) |
| Hole 4 | *sc* | (par 3) |
| Hole 5 | *or* | (par 3) |
| Hole 6 | *in* | (par 2) |
| Hole 7 | *di* | (par 1) |
| Hole 8 | *th* | (par 3) |
| Hole 9 | *fl* | (par 1) |
| Par for the course | | = 20 |

It is worthwhile to leave a large gap between the word beginning and the par in order that you can record some or most of the children's attempts.

**9** *The rules* Inform the children of the following rules:

- They will have a certain time (20 to 30 minutes is generally sufficient depending on your grade and the difficulty of the holes) within which to finish the entire course. If they fail to finish in time or leave out any holes, they will receive a triple bogey — 3 over par — for any unfinished holes.
- No proper nouns such as the names of people or products will be accepted.
- No use of dictionaries, except by the teacher.
- They may and should come to you to check on the spelling of words they are unsure of or to simply establish whether a word they have thought of is, in fact, a word.
- If the word cannot be found in the standard dictionary used in the room, then it will not be accepted.
- Any word that is found to be spelled incorrectly at the end of the game because the person concerned hasn't bothered to have it checked receives a triple bogey for that hole.
- The game should be conducted with golfing etiquette, that is, they should play quietly, wait their turn when checking words with the teacher, and no cheating!
- The golfing umpire's decision is final and no discussion will be permitted.

**10** *The scorecard* Issue the children with a scoring sheet similar to the one shown in Figure 4.

| Hole | Par | Beginnings | Letters | Score | Name |
|---|---|---|---|---|---|
| 1 | | | | | |
| 2 | | | | | |
| 3 | | | | | |
| 4 | | | | | |
| 5 | | | | | |
| 6 | | | | | |
| 7 | | | | | |
| 8 | | | | | |
| 9 | | | | | |
| **Total:** | | | **My total:** | | |

**Figure 4**  The scoring sheet

The children would then fill in the par and beginnings columns by copying those that you have written on the board.

The next column is where they write in their letters during the game.

The score column should be filled in only after you have checked their letters or corrected them from the board.

The final column is for filling in the name of the score, for example, birdie, double bogey, etc.

(For examples of reproducible nine- and eighteen-hole course scoring sheets, refer to Appendixes 1 and 2.)

**11** *Scoring* For each hole, take examples of the children's answers and write them on the board in the space between the beginning and the par for that hole. Doing this not only reinforces spelling and vocabulary but also gives you the opportunity to introduce other golfing terms, such as *double bogey* (using two more letters than you should have), *triple bogey* (three letters over par), *eagle* (where a word is completed in two letters fewer than expected, i.e., 2 under par), and an *albatross* (this would occur when a child has managed to get a par 4 beginning in one letter — it doesn't happen often!)

**12** *A sample score sheet* A child's score sheet at the completion of a nine-hole game could look like the one shown in Figure 5.

| Hole | Par | Beginnings | Letters | Score | Name |
|---|---|---|---|---|---|
| **1** | (2) | *sp* | rain | 4 | double bogey |
| **2** | (2) | *ov* | er | 2 | par |
| **3** | (3) | *pr* | ay | 2 | birdie |
| **4** | (3) | *sc* | ared | 4 | bogey |
| **5** | (3) | *or* | e | 1 | eagle |
| **6** | (2) | *in* | to | 2 | par |
| **7** | (1) | *di* | g | 1 | par |
| **8** | (3) | *th* | at | 2 | birdie |
| **9** | (1) | *fl* | y | 1 | par |
| **Total:** | 20 | | **My total:** | 19 | |

I beat the course by 1.

**Figure 5** An example of a filled-in score sheet

**13** *A summary* Well, that's basically the game of word golf. My main reason for describing it in such detail is that I consider it to be a terrific introduction and lead-in to bean-bag golf and golf in general. Word golf provides the children with a basic but sound understanding of the objectives, scoring, and some of the terminology of golf as well as introduces the troops to some golfing etiquette.

Perhaps most significant is that the children really enjoy the word golf game and are motivated by it. Utilize this enthusiasm and suggest to the children that they can make their own golf course — a bean-bag golf course.

## What is bean-bag golf?

Bean-bag golf is about using arms instead of golf clubs, bean bags instead of golf balls, and buckets or ice-cream containers instead of golf holes.

The object of the game is to try to throw the bean bag into the bucket taking as few throws as possible.

The children line up behind a tee-off marker and each child attempts to throw his or her bean bag towards and as close to a designated bucket as possible.

Given that it is difficult to throw the bean bag into the container in one throw, each child takes an initial throw, then walks up to the position where the bean bag landed. From that position the child then takes a second throw towards the hole and continues on until the bean bag has landed in the container.

On completion of the hole each child records the number of throws (or strokes) it took to get the bean bag into the container, and then moves on to the next hole and repeats the process. This continues until the course is completed and each child adds up the scores for each hole and gains a final total.

## Bean-bag golf and math — what's the connection?

The chart entitled *Bean-bag golf and math* highlights the areas of math and other aspects of learning that are incorporated in the development and playing of bean-bag golf.

# Bean-bag golf and math

## Measurement

- Measuring out and recording the length of each hole.
- Measuring and recording lengths of throws to establish the initial par for each hole.
- Specific examples:
  — weight of a bean bag
  — length of the entire golf course
  — height of the hole flags
  — volume and capacity of the containers being used as golf holes
- Measuring the length of real golf strokes, e.g., ". . . Greg Norman has hit that drive 260 m down the fairway — what a shot!" (Take the troops outside and find out how long a hit that is!) The TV and newspapers are sources for these details.

## Problem solving

- Planning and making a model of the golf course.
- Sorting and classifying a large number of hole designs to form a complete course.
- Planning and designing a map of the course and a scorecard to be used by all players.
- Organizing a round of golf for a number of children, with the children planning and implementing all details: bean bags, scorecards, equipment, who is playing with whom, which groups are starting at which holes, and dealing with any other details as they may arise.
- Identifying and addressing problems that may have come up before or during the playing of a round.
- Making graphs, keeping results, and generally noting any details that may assist in a smoother or more efficient organization of the occasions when bean-bag golf is played.

## Language, math, and golf

- Introducing a wide range of new vocabulary and terminology associated with the game of golf. (Much detailed and specific discussion will result from the group and whole-grade tasks.) The word golf game gives the children a chance to increase their vocabulary and word-building skills.
- Reading and discussing books, magazines, encyclopedias, or articles from daily newspapers that feature information on the playing of or even the history of golf. Possibly, presenting a talk or mini-project on the history, rules, and playing of golf.
- Reading and understanding the golf scorecard.
- Preparing and writing reports and articles to be placed in the school newsletter.
- Preparing and writing invitations for other grades to play bean-bag golf.

## Number

- Counting the number of throws/strokes taken for each hole; then adding all of these up to reach a final total.
- Adding or subtracting to work out by how many strokes they have beaten the course or vice versa.
- Working out the average number of strokes taken for each hole by dividing a total score by 9 or 18, depending on the size of the course.
- Working out the average number of strokes taken at a specific hole, e.g., if twenty-four children played hole 3, all their scores for that hole would be added and divided by 24, and the answer compared with the par for hole 3.
- Mentally calculating for situations such as working out strokes needed to beat par for a hole or for the course.
- Estimating the total of own and opponent's score during the game.

## Spatial relations and visual representation

- Making sketch maps/designs for each of the holes. These need to be measured accurately and objects included in them drawn to scale.
- Making an accurate map of the school with buildings, courts, equipment, and other items drawn to scale. This map should include a layout of all the golf holes.
- Representing their scores for a round of golf on a line graph. This information may be interpreted to determine things like handicaps for some.
- You could also obtain some golf clubs and show them to the children. Let them examine the angles of the clubs and ask them to explain why they range from nearly flat (approx. 20 degrees for a wedge or number 9 iron) to sharp (approx. 75 degrees for a wood or number 2 or 3 iron). Discuss their responses and angles in general.

## Cooperative group work

- Planning, designing, and sketching a number of golf holes (working in pairs).
- As a group, determining the final eighteen holes for the course. (By the nature of their task, this group will need to work closely together to make decisions and resolve differences.)
- In small groups, being responsible for such tasks as:
  - setting up of the equipment for a game;
  - organizing all the necessary arrangements for a round of golf, e.g., setting up the bean bags and scoring cards for groups of golfers;
  - collecting and storing equipment used in the game;
  - checking, graphing, and recording scores from the competitors and interpreting these data to make resultant changes to any aspect of the game.

The social skills that are developed through playing bean-bag golf are most worthwhile. Patience, observing the rules and etiquette of golf, and generally applying the manners and responsibility for a safe and enjoyable game may all be developed.

# Getting started

Discuss the idea of setting up a nine- or eighteen-hole golf course around the school. Talk about real-life golf courses and the types of holes they may have, then either draw some examples of possible holes on the board or have some of the children do this. Discuss how the longer holes are generally par 4 or 5 holes, while the shorter, but tricky, holes are usually par 3 holes.

## Designing some golf holes

Following the discussion on hole designs, tell the children that, in pairs, they are going to go outside and design at least two or three holes. Set definite boundaries where the would-be hole designers should not go. This may be for safety or practical reasons. Ask the children to work in pairs and take outside with them pencils, paper, and something to lean the paper on. Before they actually go outside, emphasize the following points:

- The designs (in the form of sketches) should *clearly* show where on the school grounds the holes are located.
- The designs should show where each hole starts (the tee-off position) and finishes (where the hole and flag will be placed).
- Each pair could try to work out what the par for each of their designs may be, although this is not essential. (*Hint:* It may be an idea to have some trundle wheels available for measuring the length of holes.)
- The designs should be accurate and include any and all permanent objects, as they may prove to be interesting hazards that could help to determine the par for the holes (e.g., trees, seats, play equipment).
- The hole designs should be practical.

Some of the holes designed by my troops would have had Greg Norman shaking in his golf shoes. One involved climbing halfway up a big tree to tee off — definitely not practical.

## Selecting the holes

If you have twelve or thirteen or more pairs of children out designing and sketching two or three golf holes per pair, then my sophisticated math skills tell me that you will end up with well over the eighteen holes required. Rather than having to make the decision yourself on which holes should be eliminated to bring the number down to eighteen, and in so doing undoubtedly disappoint somebody, have someone else do this dirty work for you — form a committee!

It then becomes the specific responsibility of this committee to choose a final eighteen holes that will ultimately become your school's own golf course. When attempting to select these final eighteen holes, the committee should undertake the following:

- Eliminate those holes that are impractical or simply don't make sense.
- Eliminate those holes that are not within the boundaries you set and so are either unsafe or not suitable.
- Eliminate any holes that do not clearly show the location of the hole or are clearly inaccurate in their location details.
- Eliminate any holes that are poorly presented.
- Choose those designs that depict interesting and practical holes.

At this point the committee may still not have reduced the number of designs to eighteen, and it may now be an opportune time to advise them to try to place the designs in an order such that they start at hole 1, go to hole 2, etc., all the the way through to hole 18. Ask the committee, or have a whole-grade discussion on how they think a real golf course is laid out. If there are few responses, ask the children whether it would be a large distance from the end of one hole to the start of the next. They will soon appreciate that it would be a good idea to have the start of each hole (tee-off position) as close as possible to the finish of the preceding hole.

Armed with this knowledge, the committee should now attempt to place the hole designs in an order that takes account of starting and finishing positions, and in so doing they will possibly be able to discount further holes. As their teacher, you may be required to *consult* with the committee and you may still need to help them in discarding certain holes. (*Hint*: Five people is a good number to have on this committee, ensuring a lot of discussion (and argument); the odd number also allows a vote to be taken to decide an issue.)

## A testing course? — Test the course first!

Now that the committee has reached agreement on a *possible* final eighteen holes, they should be encouraged to go outside and physically test the viability of the eighteen designs they have selected. Have them work out what items they will need, or inform them that they could find things such as a bean bag, a trundle wheel, and some pencils and paper very handy when checking out the designs.

With their equipment and hole designs (placed in order), the committee can now take to the school grounds and test out each of the individual designs to check the following:

- That each of the designs does, in fact, work. The tee-off position is not on the roof of the boys' bathroom. No one has to throw over a building to get to a hole. You don't have to walk through the school lunchroom to get to the next tee-off position. The hole is not 500 meters long and would take you fifteen throws just to reach the flag!
- That their layout of the holes in order works and that players don't need to walk long distances from the end of one hole to the start of the next.

Where the committee noted and marked problems with the individual hole designs or whole-course layout they should do the following:

1   Based on their testing of the designs, they should make any alterations necessary to improve individual holes. This could include things such as:

- lengthening or shortening a hole to make it practicable;
- altering the proposed position of the containers to make the hole more interesting or playable;
- altering the proposed position of the tee-off so it is closer to the finish of the previous hole or so it renders the hole more practicable;
- any other alterations they deem necessary.

2   Based on their testing, the committee may decide it is warranted to design a completely new hole. This may occur where:

- the hole simply doesn't work, but a hole is needed in that location to fit in with the proposed layout;
- the hole doesn't work, but the location of the hole is such that a workable and interesting hole can readily be designed in close proximity to the original one;
- a new hole is required because there is too long a distance between the finish and start of two consecutive holes and there is space to incorporate a new hole between them.

On completion of these alterations/new designs, the committee should again venture outside and retest the course and make further adjustments if necessary.

(*Hint*: I found it worthwhile for myself and a couple of children from the room to walk the proposed course with the members of the committee. I took some bean bags with me, and the troops and I were able to check out the course just as the committee members had originally done. This enabled us to offer some constructive comments to the committee. It then became their decision to act on this advice or not.)

# What next?

By this stage you now have eighteen bean-bag golf holes — on paper. The hole designs should now be able to be spread out on the carpet and form the layout of an eighteen-hole golf course that is both interesting and efficiently laid out. What is needed now is to put the final, necessary refinements to the holes.

## That's par for the course

In order to establish a total par for the course, the par for each of the eighteen individual holes needs to be accurately worked out. This may be the mission of the already operating committee or, better still, a new committee may be formed. The committee will need bean bags and trundle wheels and a clear understanding that working out the pars for the holes means working out how many throws it *should* take to get the bean bag into the container.

The committee should perform the following tasks:

1   Get an accurate idea of the par for each hole by each member of the committee playing the hole and finding the average score. This should give a reliable indication of what the par should be. (*Hint*: It may be necessary to remind the committee that the holes need to be challenging and not *too* easy.)

2   Accurately measure the holes, measuring from tee-off position to the container. These distances should be recorded and could assist the committee in working out pars by way of comparisons between holes.

3   Consider any hazards, natural or artificial, when trying to establish pars. It may be that the hole has many trees between the tee-off position and the flag, or there may be a fence or wall the player needs to throw over, or the flag may be directly behind some rocks or equipment. In instances such as these, the committee will need to take into account more than just the distance of the hole.

The committee may decide that the hazards constitute the addition of an extra stroke onto the par for that hole (they may have felt the par could be increased from a par 3 to a par 4), or they may also decide that the hazards serve to make the hole more challenging without warranting the addition of a stroke.

When they have decided on the pars for all the individual holes, after sufficient testing and consideration of distances and hazards, the committee should then total these and so arrive at a total par for the course. The par and length for each hole should be recorded. Perhaps on each of the designs would be a suitable place for this.

(The *Royal Deer Park Golf Course*, as we decided to call it, has a par for the course of a challenging but achievable 69. On average, slightly over 50% of the grade break par for the course.)

## Working out the penalties

With the pars for each hole and the course now worked out, you may now suggest to the committee that there are certain areas of the school, for example, the dumpster, parking lot, garden area, roofs of buildings, trash-bin enclosure, or any other areas that are particular to your own school, that are *out of bounds*. If any golfer lands his or her bean bag in any of those areas, then there should be a penalty of a specified number of strokes. You and the commitee should designate and agree on the areas to be specified as being *out of bounds* and the penalty, in strokes, that landing in that area would incur. To do this, it would probably prove most worthwhile for you to walk the course with the committee and make a point of noting areas such as those mentioned above:

- For example, landing your bean bag in the parking lot may cost you 2 strokes as this area would be *out of bounds*. It could be dangerous and so players should be discouraged from throwing near the parking lot by a significant penalty.
- If a bean bag lands on any roof, the penalty may be 3 strokes.
- Landing in the new garden beds may mean a 1 stroke penalty.

*Out of bounds* areas and penalties having been decided, have the children on the committee make the appropriate number of *Out of bounds* signs, for example:

---

**OUT OF BOUNDS**

**2 STROKE**

**PENALTY**

---

These signs may then be attached or tied to objects in, on, or adjacent to the designated *Out of bounds* areas.

(While walking the course with my committee, they noticed that one of the holes involved throwing over the long- and triple-jump pits, while another involved throwing over the sandpit. They decided that the sand areas were like bunkers on a real golf course, so they suggested that if anyone landed in those areas, there should be a 1 stroke penalty. Two of the holes on our course also have large rocks partly surrounding the flag and container, and it was decided that to land on these rocks would incur a 1 stroke penalty. In all these instances, the penalties were agreed to and subsequently the appropriate signs were drawn up.)

2 stroke penalty for landing your bean bag on the rock on the 6th hole.

Bunker penalty on the 5th hole.

## What's needed now?

So what do you have at the moment? You should have the design and layout for an eighteen-hole course complete with:

- a par for each individual hole;
- a total par for the course;
- length of each hole;
- designated *out of bounds* areas and associated penalties.

The course has been tried and most, if not all, problems solved, so all that is needed now are those accessories that will make the game more enjoyable and the essential equipment for the playing of the game.

The following items are attractive embellishments for the course rather than necessities, but they do add appreciably to the efficiency and presentation of the bean-bag golf course.

**1** *Hole designs* These could be placed immediately alongside the tee-off positions and could readily be mounted onto canes, sticks, or any other type of pole or post. The hole designs should include a pictorial diagram of the layout of the hole (from tee to flag), the par for the hole, the length of the hole, and any penalty that may apply for that hole.

Some examples of hole designs drawn up by children in my room are shown in the cartoon. I had yet another group of children take on the task of developing these hole designs as it gave me the opportunity to involve even more children in the development of the course. *P.S.*: Make sure your troops can spell p, e, n, a, l, t, y.

43

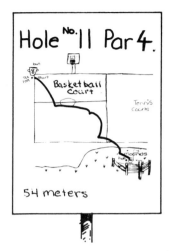 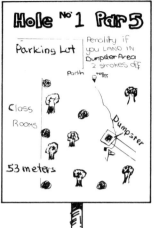 

Hole designs

All holes have a diagram of the layout of the hole.

The children who produced the hole designs utilized the original designs and layouts as developed by the initial planning committee.

The hole designs have the attributes of informing all people playing the various holes of the shape of the hole, how many strokes/throws they should take to get their bean bags in the container, how long the hole is, and any penalties that may be incurred on the hole.

This information is particularly relevant to those children from other grades who may be invited to play the course but have not previously seen it. Furthermore, the hole designs add that very worthwhile touch of professionalism to the course.

**2** *A map of the course* As for the hole designs, there may well be numerous occasions when children other than those from your grade have been invited to play the course. When this occurs, the combination of having designs for each hole and having a map showing an overall layout of the course, and the location of each hole on the course, greatly helps. New players need to know how to move about the course and so avoid confusion and build-ups of players waiting to play holes. The maps of the course could be issued to each pair, trio, or foursome who are playing together before they start their round.

Once again it was the task of another group of children in my room to design and draw up the map of the course shown in Figure 6. (A small group of three volunteered to take on this job.) They used an already available map of the school (as per the map utilized in developing the school math trail) as the basis for the map of the golf course.

44

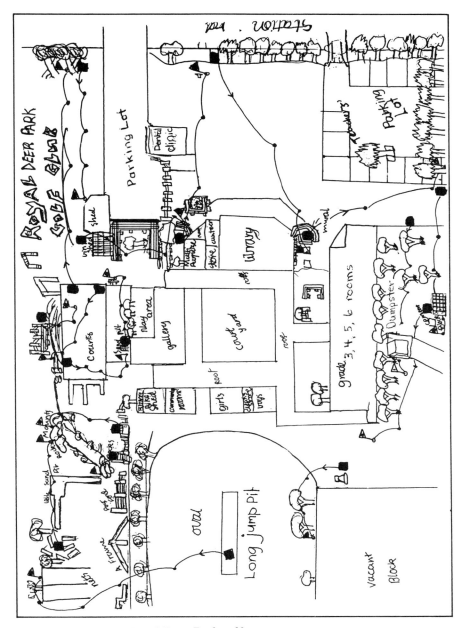

**Figure 6** Map of the Royal Deer Park golf course

As with the hole designs, this map is not absolutely vital, but nonetheless it does contribute to a more efficient operating of the course and is a very worthwhile activity for a small group of children to participate in developing.

**3  *A scorecard***  This is an essential item and a great assignment to give to yet another small group of children. To design and produce an effective, easy-to-follow scorecard is a challenging problem-solving exercise and one that the group needs to have success with.

A well-thought-out scorecard not only assists the organization of a round of golf but also means that each individual player needs to assume some responsibility for his or her own score. An effective scorecard also allows the children to monitor their progress around the course and compare how they are performing against their opponents and the course during and at the completion of a round of bean-bag golf.

The scorecard should feature the following:

- A place for the player to place his or her name.
- The hole numbers written down, 1 to 18, with the par for each hole written next to the hole number.
- Next to each of the hole numbers, a space or column where the player can write down the number of strokes taken to complete the hole.
- A space for the player to write down the final total.
- A space somewhere on the card to write down the total par for the course.
- A final feature you may wish to be included on the scorecard is a list of rules pertaining to your particular course. Examples could be: do not go into the parking lot to pick up a bean bag; do not climb trees to retrieve bean bags, ask your teacher first; do not throw your bean bags until it is safe to do so. Other rules of golf may also be included if desired.

A copy of the scorecard designed and developed by two children in my room is shown in Figure 7. Understandably, they were well pleased with their effort. This sample can be used as a guide for the development of a

## Bean - Bag Golf ☺!

| Hole Nº | Par | Your Score | Result - eg. 2 over = Double bogey (Partner 1, 2) | Hole Nº | Par | Your Score | Result - eg. 2 over = Double bogey (Partner 1, 2) |
|---|---|---|---|---|---|---|---|
| 1 | 5 | | | 10 | 4 | | |
| 2 | 4 | | | 11 | 4 | | |
| 3 | 3 | | | 12 | 5 | | |
| 4 | 5 | | | 13 | 3 | | |
| 5 | 5 | | | 14 | 4 | | |
| 6 | 3 | | | 15 | 3 | | |
| 7 | 3 | | | 16 | 3 | | |
| 8 | 3 | | | 17 | 4 | | |
| 9 | 4 | | | 18 | 4. | | |

Total for first 9 Holes ☐          Total for second 9 Holes ☐

Par for course 69.          Final total ☐

RULES
1/ Furthest away plays first.
2/ Don't start to play a hole until the group playing the hole has finished.
3/ Be patient.

RULES
4/ Be quiet when people are throwing from tee.
5/ Use your manners.

**Figure 7** Scorecard for the Royal Deer Park golf course

scorecard for your own course, or it can serve to illustrate the sort of effort the children are capable of, particularly when motivated.

**4** *The equipment* The following items will be needed to enjoy a well-organized and well-presented round of bean-bag golf.

- **Bean bags** These may be readily available from your school storeroom. If there are not enough bean bags (60 is a good number as that allows yours and another grade to play simultaneously), they can be readily purchased and are relatively inexpensive. You may even wish to make your own.

Numbered bean bags

The bean bags should then be marked (a water-resistant felt-tipped pen is best) with a number from 1 to 60, so that each golfer knows the number of his or her own bean bag before the start of a game. This

47

prevents confusion on the course and also tends to make each golfer a little more accountable and responsible for his or her bean bag.

(*Hint*: On the scorecard devised by the children in my room, they allowed for a space where each player wrote down his or her name and the number of the bean bag. At the completion of the game this enabled the children in charge of the "pro shop" in my room to check off the bean bags as they were returned. Yellow and red were found to be the best colors for bean bags — green was obviously the worst.)

*Some bean-bag facts:*
- Bean bags are physically attracted to trees.
- It is unwise to try to remove a bean bag from said trees by throwing up another bean bag.
- When the bag breaks open, there is a very large number of beans contained therein.

• **Containers**  Ice-cream containers make very good holes and can be easily acquired by asking the children to bring them from home. Small buckets are better, but being more difficult and expensive to obtain and since they would invariably have a flag stick pushed through the bottom of them, their use is not really warranted. (*Hint*: The ice-cream containers tend to split occasionally, so it is a good idea to have some extras on hand.)

Bean-bag golf holes

To assist with the setting up of the course prior to play, it is a sound idea to number each of the eighteen containers/holes beforehand.

(The children in my room brought along 1, 2, and 4 liter empty ice-cream containers and there was a great deal of discussion over which size container to use on which holes to make them that little bit harder or easier.)

• **Flag sticks**  Wooden stakes, canes sharpened at one end, metal rods, or anything else that will pierce the bottom of an ice-cream container and can be driven into the ground will suffice for a flag stick. The flag sticks hold down the containers and prevent them from overturning or moving on windy days or when a bean bag lands in them.

48

- **Flags**   The flags can be made by the troops from cloth or vinyl. They will need eighteen flags with one of the numbers 1 to 18 painted on each. Black numbers on light-colored vinyl seem to work the most effectively. The flags may be attached to the flagsticks with tape or string. A small group can design and make the flags.

  The flags are more than a pleasing aesthetic aspect of the golf course. They also designate, from a distance, the number and location of the hole and this may prevent golfers from playing the incorrect hole.
- **Markers**   While not essential, markers can be used to designate where a particular player's bean bag has landed. This is relatively important as a player may need to stop and wait for another player in the same group to have his or her throw.

  Large counters make good markers. The counters could be marked with one of the numbers from 1 to 60 so that they match the number of the bean bag issued to a player. Once again, this would avoid confusion on the course.

# Let's play golf!

Well, we now have a golf course complete with hole designs, a map of the course, and a scorecard. We also have numbered bean bags, flags, and ice-cream container holes as well as flagsticks. So let's get out there and hit the course. Before rushing into it and having twenty-six eager students, and a perhaps equally eager teacher, all standing impatiently and more than a little agitated at the first tee waiting to go, a little pre-planning may be very worthwhile.

Assigning the following organizational tasks to groups or pairs of children will hopefully avoid the first tee crush and other problems as well.

Once again these are challenging, practical problem-solving exercises, particularly organizing a round. While I have indicated possible solutions/methods, the children should be given the opportunity to discover these for themselves with minimal assistance from you, the teacher.

## Organizing a round

Either choose or call for two or three volunteers whose task is to organize the bean bags and scorecards so that the players know who they will be playing with, what number bean bag they will be using, and what hole on the golf course they will be starting at.

While it will largely depend on the volunteers, and how much well-worded advice you give them, the task of organizing the class to play golf can generally be achieved by the following:

- Dividing the grade randomly (but not so randomly that you have people playing together whom you think definitely should not be) into groups of two, three, or four, depending on the number of children in your room. (Three is perhaps the best number to have playing a round of golf.)
- Assigning each group to a particular hole; for example: Brendan, Jane, and Leanne start at hole 1; Alicia, Con, and James start at hole 3. By starting the groups at alternate holes, there is less chance of groups having to wait for groups ahead to finish the hole before they can play.
- Taking bean bags randomly from the container and assigning them directly to the players; for example: Brendan — bean bag 17, Jane — bean bag 24, etc.

This information may now be directly transferred to the scorecard with the number of the starting hole written in the top right-hand corner:

## BEAN-BAG GOLF        (1)
## Number of bean bag: 17
## Name: Brendan

- It now becomes a matter of calling up each group and issuing them their bean bags and scorecards and informing them of the hole they will be starting at.

If another grade joins yours and there may be up to sixty children playing a game, this type of organization is essential. The groups can still remain at three or four in size, although it will be necessary to disperse the players among more holes on the course.

It is also a very good idea to have at least one person from your own grade with each group; this person will have a very good idea of the layout of the course, the penalties, the scoring, the basic play, and general etiquette (dealt with later) of bean-bag golf and subsequently can pass on this knowledge to the new players.

### Setting up the course

With the players now organized for a round of golf, the next task is to give them somewhere to play. Setting up the course entails the following:

- Collecting and distributing the holes (ice-cream containers) and flag sticks to their appointed positions on the school grounds. This can be effectively achieved by having a group of six children, each to be responsible for obtaining three designated holes and flag sticks (e.g., Sandy knows she's in charge of finding containers 1, 2, and 3 and flag sticks 1, 2, and 3) and setting them up.

It is obviously very important for the members of this group to clearly know the layout of the course and exactly where the containers/holes should be positioned.

- Collecting and distributing the hole designs to their appointed positions on the golf course. Once again, this can be achieved by having a group in charge of the operation. A group of three children should have six designs each (e.g., Kevin collects the hole designs 1 to 6, Angie collects the designs for holes 7 to 12, etc.) to place in appropriate locations alongside the tee-off positions. As for the flag sticks group, a sound knowledge of the course layout is essential.
- Collecting and distributing the penalty signs to their correct positions on the course. A group of three is probably sufficient to take on this task efficiently. They will need to know which holes have penalties associated with them and on what objects or in what places the signs should be attached or placed.
- Having one or two children who know the layout extremely well to check the course when all the collecting and distributing has been completed. They may need to reposition a container or move a sign or make any other adjustments as necessary.

Initially it may take the troops as long as 20 minutes to set up the course, but this time tends to reduce as the children become more familiar with the course and more efficient at collecting and distributing.

(*Hint*: Using a waterproof paint, a member of the original committee and I painted the tee-off positions on the ground in the form of the number of the hole written inside a triangle (see illustration). This greatly assisted the setting up of the course and also aided new players in finding their way around the course.

Triangle is painted on the ground to help in setting up the course and finding your way about the course.

## Golf etiquette

This is a vital component of bean-bag golf. Knowing and applying golf etiquette not only helps to establish and maintain order and control around the course but also develops very worthwhile social skills.

Discussion of the actual game of golf and having the troops try to decide what sorts of rules or behavior should apply on a golf course may result in the children arriving at some of the actual rules of golfing etiquette that apply in real golf and should apply to bean-bag golf also.

Where they don't arrive at basic etiquette, such as the farthest from the hole always plays first or no one starts to play a hole until the group ahead has finished, explain or better still have the children explain the reasoning behind these forms of etiquette.

The group designing the scorecard for my grade decided to include what they considered the five important rules or forms of etiquette. These may be found in the middle pages of the scorecard (p. 47).

Applying golfing etiquette becomes particularly pertinent when another grade has been invited to play. The children from your room should be asked to set the example in terms of appropriate behavior on the course and encourage the new players to do so also.

## Playing the game

The only way to fully appreciate the worth and enjoyment of a round of bean-bag golf is to either get out there and join the troops in a round or move around the various holes and simply observe the children going about their game.

Undoubtedly, problems such as bean bags up trees or over fences and children forgetting to apply proper golfing etiquette will occur during a round. You may have to help solve and adjudicate on some of these problems, but generally the effort put into getting the game off and running is well worth it.

## Clearing up the course

The game is over, the scores have been added up and comparisons made, hard-luck stories and individual incidents have been regurgitated and exaggerated, and the children are generally feeling pretty good. What a shame that now the course has to be cleaned up!

You can either have the whole grade go out and collect some gear and return it, then have a selected group go and check if any containers or signs or anything else has been left. The other alternative is to have a group of five or six children collect, check off, and neatly pack away all the equipment ready for the next round.

## A private or public course?

The idea of inviting other grades to come and play the course has previously been mentioned. To share the golf course with others is a good thing in that it allows the children who designed, put together, and operate the course to show off what they have achieved. Furthermore, the organizational and planning skills required by the children in having other people play are considerable. Finally, having a public rather than a private course provides you and your grade with the opportunities to conduct and host events such as:

- running an open event for all the children in the grade to compete on an individual basis;
- having grade challenges, where the lowest average whole-grade score wins;
- inviting parents to play the course with their children during education week, children's week, or other similar events;
- inviting other schools to come and play bean-bag golf — this can occur as part of a social inter-school sport day or as a sport alternative component of a school exchange day;
- any other event you or your children may think of.

# Evaluation

When evaluating bean-bag golf, perhaps the best way is to analyze the game in terms of the following:

**1 *Cooperation*** This is probably the most important aspect as it is the teamwork involved in planning the course; choosing, reviewing, and improving the holes; organizing a round; gathering, distributing, and collecting the equipment and generally working on any problems that arise in making the golf course work.

No single group or person can set up and operate the course. It takes a concerted, whole-grade effort, for which cooperation and successful interaction between the children in the room are essential. Normally the motivation behind playing the game is sufficient to ensure that the troops work productively together as a coordinated unit.

Nonetheless, monitor how effectively the various groups and pairs do cooperate and work to the same goal and note anecdotally any child or children who may be inhibiting this cooperative process.

Conversely, note also those children who actively promote the notion of teamwork and display the leadership and direction that some of the other children may require.

**2 *Responsibility*** Throughout the whole process of setting up and playing the game, the children are, by necessity, left to work and play independently. To do so without causing trouble means not only that the troops are motivated and realize the importance of everybody doing his or her part but also that the children are displaying the necessary responsibility and maturity.

If the children cannot display the ability to work efficiently, without constant supervision, and play the game effectively and independently, then as well as having something to evaluate on a whole-grade or group or individual basis, you will also have a large headache in trying to get a game of bean-bag golf going!

**3 *Problem solving*** In the setting up and running of the course, there are numerous logistical, physical, and organizational problems that will inevitably occur. Before wading in to assist and offer advice, sit back and observe how the children cope with these problems. As long as it won't prove too costly, give the children the opportunity to learn from their mistakes.

Look for the group dynamics, the thought processes, the various strategies applied, and how or if the knowledge or solutions are shared.

Observing children in these situations can prove invaluable. The non-classroom environment and practical nature of most of the problems that arise often put the problems into a logical, commonsense context and to observe and note just who does or who does not cope or adjust in these situations is very enlightening.

**4** *Mathematical* Rather than anything too complex and clinical, which tends to focus on what the children can't do or are having difficulty with, try looking for those children who are displaying improved mathematical understanding, knowledge, and skill in the more practical and pertinent situation of bean-bag golf.

Division may have come alive through working on averages; using materials may have improved measurement skills; communication skills may have been developed out of a need to be an effective member of a group; given a purpose, mapping and designing skills may have improved; an increased willingness to take risks in the less threatening environment of a group developing a golf course may have developed; number skills may have improved through the practical applications of the scorecard.

These are only some of the wide range of mathematical attributes that you may wish to look for in the children when observing them in a specifically mathematical way.

Perhaps the most relevant and important observation to make is whether the children are enjoying the math involved in bean-bag golf and as a result are adopting a positive or more positive attitude towards math.

**5** *Competitiveness* Evaluate the level of enjoyment and satisfaction experienced by the players during and after a game. If any problems lie in the competitive nature of the game, reinforce that the real competition is to improve each person's score and try to beat the course.

The players should be encouraged to compare scores independently of each other, or simply work out — better still have the troops work out — a fair handicap system for *any* children who are struggling with the course.

**6** *Other* Improvement in throwing skills, the development of social skills and golfing etiquette, knowledge of the game of golf, and a general sense of achievement and enjoyment are all factors you may wish to consider and evaluate in the children.

# Summary

Bean-bag golf is an interactive, large-scale problem-solving activity that combines fresh air, enjoyment, exercise, and real-life math.

Apart from the cooperation and social skills that it engenders, one of the main features of bean-bag golf is the ownership of the course and the organization of the game by the children themselves. Throughout the development and eventual operating of the course, the children are encouraged to take responsibility for themselves and the ultimate results, and it is this ownership that proves highly motivational to the children.

Ultimately, it will be in the improved attitudes toward and increased awareness of mathematics displayed by the children that the value of bean-bag golf will be appreciated.

## WORD GOLF: NINE-HOLE COURSE

| Hole | Par | Beginnings | Letters | Score | Name |
|------|-----|------------|---------|-------|------|
| 1 | | | | | |
| 2 | | | | | |
| 3 | | | | | |
| 4 | | | | | |
| 5 | | | | | |
| 6 | | | | | |
| 7 | | | | | |
| 8 | | | | | |
| 9 | | | | | |
| Total: | | | My total: | | |

**Appendix 1**  Nine-hole golf score sheet

# WORD GOLF: EIGHTEEN-HOLE COURSE

| Hole | Par | Beginnings | Letters | Score | Name |
|------|-----|-----------|---------|-------|------|
| 1 | | | | | |
| 2 | | | | | |
| 3 | | | | | |
| 4 | | | | | |
| 5 | | | | | |
| 6 | | | | | |
| 7 | | | | | |
| 8 | | | | | |
| 9 | | | | | |
| 10 | | | | | |
| 11 | | | | | |
| 12 | | | | | |
| 13 | | | | | |
| 14 | | | | | |
| 15 | | | | | |
| 16 | | | | | |
| 17 | | | | | |
| 18 | | | | | |
| Total: | | | My total: | | |

**Appendix 2**   Eighteen-hole golf score sheet

| Object or place | Location | Question | Answer |
|---|---|---|---|
|  |  |  |  |

**Appendix 3**  Question sheet for the school math trail

58

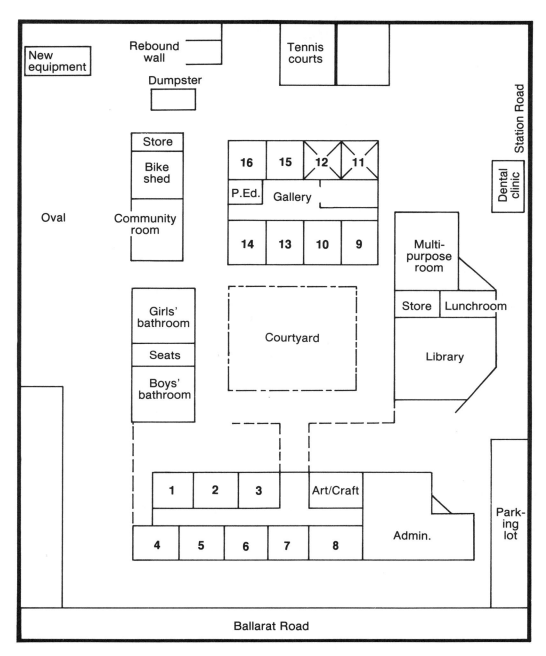

**Appendix 4**  Map of my school

59

| Question | Working-out space | Answer |
|----------|-------------------|--------|
|          |                   |        |

**Appendix 5** Question and answer sheet to accompany the map

60